Difficult Riddles for Smart Kids

300 of the Best Difficult Riddles and Brain Teasers to Exercise Your Mind while Having Fun!

Table Of Contents

Introduction

Unlike corduroy pants, riddles have been entertaining people for a longer amount of time. They've been around ever since man began to think for himself; which is sometimes said to go before recorded history.

Today, you won't have to answer to an angry statue in order to enjoy a good riddle. Different people from different cultures have hundreds of thousands of brain teasers that test your imagination and your logic.

Spending time on riddles and brain teasers helps you keep your mind sharp. This is because you're more keen on details you may have missed and you listen or read more intently, making sure your understanding is clear in order to answer accurately.

Some riddles are solved with a little math. Some are solved with a simple but creative solution. Some are solved by simply looking out of the box. Some riddles are designed to confuse and mislead you

In this book, you will find 300 hard riddles which are sure to keep you occupied (as long as you don't take a peek at the answer key). They make for great conversation starters and quick past-times to blow off a few minutes.

Take note, though, that you will have to flip through the chapters of the riddles before you get to the chapters of their answers. In a way, you would still have to work a little hard to get to the answers you seek. Or, if you want to have it the easy way, each riddle has a link that would lead you straight to the answer. Have fun with these twisters and see yourself become smarter. Thank you!

Chapter 1 Difficult Riddles

If this is your first time dealing with riddles, or you've gotten rusty, this is the place to start. Although this is a section for difficult riddles, this first chapter is a collection of the easiest ones of the bunch.

1. What do you have to break before you can make use of it?

2. What starts off tall when it's young but becomes short when it's older?

3. What has so many holes but still manages to hold water?

4. What is the one question to which you can never say "yes" to?

5. What is always impossible to see but is constantly right in front of you?

6. What can be broken even if you don't do anything with it?

7. What is the one thing that will always go up but will definitely never go down?

8. Who shaves almost everyday but never has to shave at all?

9. What has plenty of branches but not fruit or leaves or even a trunk?

10. What becomes harder to see when there is more of it around you?

11.   hat is so light yet you cannot hold it for so long?

12.   Where is the one place that yesterday comes after today?

13.   What can never move but always goes down and up?

14.   What has four legs but only one foot?

15.   What can you never throw but only catch?

16.   What cannot bite at all even when it has teeth?

17.   What possesses a tail as well as a head, but doesn't have a body?

18.   What has thirteen hearts and nothing else?

19.   What kind of coat should you always put on while wet?

20.   What has four wheel and flies as well?

21.   What could be so sensitive that it could break with a breath?

22.   What is the one thing that can occupy a whole room yet not take up any space at all?

23.   What is something that doesn't break but always fall?

24.   What is something that always falls but doesn't break?

25.   What has mountains with no stones, cities without buildings and even oceans with no water?

26.   What is the one thing that will always be yours but everyone is going to have to use?

27.   What is the only thing on this planet that becomes more wet the more it dries?

28.   What will never happen in a thousand years but will happen twice in a moment?

29.   What never gets wet but is always seen in the water?

30.   When you take more of this, you leave even more behind. What is it?

31.   What will perish when you offer it a drink, but will flourish if you offer it a dish?

32.   What cries without any eyes, hovers without any propeller, and always comes with darkness?

33.   What goes around the world but never leaves its place?

34.   What does the poor have that the rich desire? If you eat it, though, you won't live.

35.   What is something that end with T, also begins with T, and also has T in it?

36.   What thing will always break when on water; but will never break on land?

37. What is something that you always measure; but you cannot even see?

38. What contraption will allow anyone to see what is beyond any wall without breaking the wall?

39. What is something that seems to never ask a question but is always being answered?

40. What is a box that contains plenty of keys that don't open any doors or locks?

41. What do you call a building with the most stories among all other buildings?

42. It loses its head during the mornings, but finds it again come night time. What is it?

43.   What becomes bigger whenever it becomes shorter?

44.   What is something the left hand may hold but the right hand may not?

45.   Its white when its's filthy but black once it's cleaned. What is it?

46.   The more you of this you take away, the larger it will only get. What is it?

47.   This will go up a chimney when it's at the bottom, but cannot come down the chimney when it's at the top?

48.   You can always count on them when things go wrong. What are they?

49. This owns a neck but doesn't have a head. What is it?

50. Out of all the words in the dictionary, one is always spelled wrong. What is it?

51. This starts as an odd number. But if you remove one letter, it becomes even. What number is this?

52. What is the farthest a rabbit can hop into the woods?

53. If three is a crowd and two is company, what do you call four and five?

54. What is one word that suddenly turns shorter when two letters are added to it?

55.   Leopards have plenty of spots. What can it do to change them?

56.   You never eat them but you buy them for dinner. What are they?

57.   This is in the middle of April and the middle of March, but you won't find it in the beginning of either. What is it?

58.   There is an English word that has not one, not two, but three double-letters laid out after each other. What is this word?

59.   What is surrounded by wood, comes from a mine, and is used by everyone?

60. What eats this thing also gets eaten. What is it?

61. This was the highest mountain on planet Earth before mount Everest was discovered. What is it?

62. A young boy just turned ten during his last birthday party, but will turn twelve on the next. How did that happen?

63. The wind brings this to life but it has no body. It can talk without mouth and hears without ears. What is it?

64. In a boat, you find about 50 people. It doesn't sink, but you cannot see a single person. What happened?

65. What is contains a thousand letters but is only seven letters long?

66. What goes up but shall never grow and is taller than the trees?

67. This needs air but cannot breathe. It grows but doesn't live. What is it?

68. What do you do to make the number one disappear by only adding a letter?

69. It lives when we sing, yet dies after the song. What is it?

70. It's quite easy to get into. However, it is quite difficult to get out of. What is it?

71. This flies despite having no wings. It bites despite having no teeth. What is it?

72. With this, you go when you see red, but you will certainly stop when you see green. What is it?

73. What gets smaller every time it bathes?

74. This starts as black when you buy it. It turns red when you use it. And when it turns gray, it is thrown away. What is it?

75. This goes in the water as black, but is red when it comes out. What is it?

76. What is very heavy when it is forward, but is not when it is backward?

77.   What is a musical instrument you can use and hear, but never touch nor see?

78.   This smells foul when alive but then smells so good when it's dead. What is it?

79.   This cannot be drowned in water. But it will not burn either even if you put it in fire. What is it?

80.   This will not die even when thrown off a building, but will perish when given water. What is it?

81.   What becomes harder to catch the faster you run after it?

82.   This is an animal called the animal it eats. What is it?

83.   In here, you are not a guest, neither are you a trespasser. What is it?

84.   What is always running but it never walks. It sings sometimes, but it never talks.

85.   When you take off its skin, it will not cry; you will. What is it?

86.   What language is never spoken in any part of the world?

87.   This can make two of everything it sees. What is it?

88.   Although this has two hands, neither of them can scratch myself. What is it?

89.   You can crack it, make it, play it, and even tell it. What is it?

90.   This lives in a house with no doors and no windows. It is all alone. If it wants to go out it has to break its house. What is it?

91.   It has a thumb and four fingers, but doesn't have any blood. What is it?

92.   What is something that has plenty of needles but can't sew?

93.   What is something that runs around the whole house but never leaves?

94.   What acts like a cat and looks like a cat but isn't a cat?

95.   This has many faces and follows you at night. What is it?

96.   What is six letters long but becomes twelve when you take away one letter?

97.   This is found with kittens as well as mittens. You find it in scarves and socks too! What is it?

98.   It's a small pool surrounded by two walls. One wall is white and soft while the other is dark and hairy. What is it?

99.   What is something that never was, but is always to be. Not one person can see it, but everyone knows it's there?

100. It is very pretty as it flies in the sky, but before that, it lives in the dirt. What is it?

101. This can either be complex or simple. It has a name but no body. It always has an answer but can be difficult to find. What is it?

102. Whether you use this a lot or not at all, you change this every month. What is it?

103. It is the end of sickness but the start of sadness. You also cannot have happiness without two of it. What is it?

104. This passes in front of the sun but doesn't make any shadow. What is it?

105.   What happens so fast that no one sees it, but anyone can see right through it?

106.   This is something people use, but not all the time. Some may forget about it and some remember for all of time. It's used to make money. It can't be picked up from the ground and cannot be thrown into the ocean. What is it?

107.   What is bright when it points upward but dark when it points downward?

108.   This is a ruler of the shovels that also has a wife. He is very thin and has a twin. What is he?

109.   When this bites something, they don't bleed. It has to be pushed for it to bite. It brings it's victims together. What is it?

110.   This keeps you healthy but can kill you as well. It's inside of you already but can take your breath away. What is it?

111.   It isn't a place but you visit it quite often and either smile or cry. What is it?

112.   What is a doll but not meant for children? It always stands straight but lies down when it's windy. It's a dumb doll but works very hard. What is it?

113.   What can surely fill an entire room but also fill an entire heart? If you have it, you cannot share it. When you share it, you lose it. What is it?

114.   This is a word pronounced as a letter but has three of them. While it has three letters you only use two. What is it?

115. You cannot see this but it can most certainly see you. It sees so well it sees right past through you. What is it?

116. What word means life spelled forward, but becomes bad when spelled backwards?

117. This is a natural place when read as a word. When one letter is removed, it becomes a man-made place. What is it?

118. What can fit in well in the right places, but cannot talk at all. It helps make picture, but cannot see anything. What is it?

119. What is flat but very deep? It vast but gives food as well. It's calm at times but angry at some. What is it?

120. What can hurt and at the same time help? You can either see them or read them but you can't touch them.

121. The more you see of this, the less you see. What is it?

122. What has many folds that stands on the ground but reaches the sky?

123. You dry this first then you wet it. The longer it swims the better it gets. What is it?

124. This is the start of a long list, the beginning of a common song, and always first in line. It's in cars but not in busses. What is it?

125. What is lighter than what makes it up. There is more to this than meets the eye. What is it?

126. What cannot fly but has four wings? It moves all day long but never leaves its place.

127. This is seen when you look up. It's also when you look out past the beach. It's four letters long. What is it?

128. What is not a gossip but has dirt on everyone? It has a big mouth but never talks.

129. This is under your skin but outside your thoughts. What is it?

130. What is fat when you need it but flat when you don't? You sound funny when you kiss it.

131.   What is something that everyone sees but ignores. When you look at it, you don't focus on it.

132.   This has a tail but no feet, and ears but no eyes. It can hear everything you say and shouts back at you. What is it?

133.   What has a tongue but no mouth? You're inside of it and outside of it as well.

134.   This has almost a million ribs and just two spines. What is it?

135.   What can go from here to there simply by showing up?

136.   What has a hard heart but such a soft body?

137.   Cool enough for beer, but hot enough for tea. It caresses beaches but cuts rock. What is it?

138.   What has arms but no fingers? Has legs but cannot run?

139.   What takes you force to open this can open with a touch. What is it?

140.   What plays with strings but isn't a musician? It leaves a trail wherever it goes.

141.   It never lies and never hides but has no eyes nor mouth. It body but comes in different shapes. What is it?

142.   What always comes back to you even if you throw it away?

143.   This has nine letters but has space inside for several more if you want. What is it?

144.   This has feathers and can fly, but doesn't have any wings. It has a head and a body but it's not a bird. What is it?

145.   What is round or square, long or short, bought or grown, painted or naked?

146.   If you poke its eyes it will open and eat. It eats paper, string, cloth and everything you can fit. What is it?

147.   What is pretty in spring as it wears a full coat? In winter it takes off its coat and in summer it wears more.

148. It is helpless without you. You need to help it turn a new leaf. It has a spine but no conviction. It is pale but always has something to say. What is it?

149. The more light there is the more different its shape is. Different lights make it change erratically. What is it?

150. Leave it be and it slowly dies. Flip it and it lives again. It sets time for you but doesn't tell time. What is it?

151. This is half water and half carbon. It is also poisonous to fish. What is it?

152. It's as long as ten men but ten men can't break it but a little boy can play with it. What is it?

153. It goes from house to house and brings messengers and mailmen safely. When it's raining, it stays outside. What is it?

154. Never seen on the ground but always in the air. It's not in France, but is also in Spain as well as hail and mis. What is it?

155. This is food spelled with three letters. Take one away and it still sounds the same. What is it?

156. Taken from its mother, it is beaten and burned. Then it becomes something used everyday. What is it?

157. It has a red cap on its head and a stone in its throat. What is it?

158. Done with one hand, it takes some time. It's used for words and not lines. What is it?

159. This group of things go together. One sits down and keeps the other two. The other keeps eating but is never full while the third runs away and never comes back. What are they?

160. Always ready for work, it has legs but no head. You can use it for hours and it never tires. What is it?

161. I man did the same as this, he will break his back. This isn't rich but leaves a glistening trail. What is it?

162. What moves by request with two rings? It just rests if our mixture isn't right.

163.   This can be green, yellow, or even red. You still like them in any color. What is it?

164.   When young, it is sweet. When mature, it is classy. When old, it is expensive. What is it?

165.   She seems full whenever you see her at night, but she will never give birth. What is she?

166.   What lies for you but brings out your confidence?

167.   Go one way, and it's loose. Go the other and it's tight. Go left for in. Go right for out. What is it?

168.   This liquid is used by all but drunk by none. When it's burned it gives life. What is it?

169.   What is a box without a key with a golden wet treasure hidden within?

170.   What is the combination of a beaver, otter, and a duck?

171.   What is sometimes white and sometimes black? To where it takes you, you cannot go back.

172.   What has four legs and no tail and a concert every night?

173.   It runs great lengths but rests under a bed. It never runs alone and has a tongue. What is it?

174.   This one runs but never walks. When it runs people stay clear. What is it?

175. They die as soon as they are born. You cannot count them but you can feel them. What are they?

176. Drawn from its mother then left to dry. Stored in a cave until it becomes gold to eat. What is it?

177. What is a small house full of food but no door to enter nor window to peek?

178. It's a word that means barely there. Take away one letter and it becomes a herb. What is it?

179. What is a woman that can marry three different men but never need a divorce?

180. This marks the end and not a start. It's heavy and hard but written on. What is it?

181. Here, you have a black seed planted in white land. What is it?

182. When given, it is worthless. When offered, always rejected. What is it?

183. What comes in a can but can also come in as a punch?

184. It's dirty but much desired. When found it's broken up and burned. What is it?

185. When alive they're quite quiet but when dead they're quite noisy. What are they?

186. What is the only word that has all 26 letters but has only three syllables?

187. What starts with gas yet only has ten letters?

188. There's two in every corner, but only one in a room. What is it?

189. What fruit becomes a crime if you remove the first letter?

190. This house is full of gold but no man has made it. There are sentries at the door but no guards. What is it?

191. If you make it, you don't tell it. If you take it, you don't know it. If you know it, you don't want it. What is it?

192. This is at the front of a woman, but in the back of a cow. What is it?

193.   What comes from water but dies when placed in water?

194.   What can move when tied up but needs to stay put when untied?

195.   What food has no beginning, middle, nor end?

196.   This begins and ends with E but is full of beautiful countries. What is it?

197.   A large field of ears but cannot hear a thing. What is it?

198.   It goes off almost every morning but never leaves its place after going off. What is it?

199.   What cannot be kept until given?

200. It is worth more than gold but hard to find. Easy to lose but costs nothing to get. What is it?

201. What word still has some left even after you take away its whole?

202. This has a bed but never sleeps; a head but never weeps. What is it?

203. What is covered with hair and has 8 spares?

204. What is a person that builds golden crowns and silver bridges?

205. This only touches one person but binds two. What is it?

206. It's a fruit with one seed but is also in calendars. What is it?

Chapter 2 Extremely Difficult Riddles

Congratulations on making it this far! If you're still raring for more at this point, that would mean the earlier riddles were a little too soft for your taste. A bigger challenge awaits among these pages...

1.   You are locked in a room in which you have to escape. There is only a shovel inside the room. The only two ways out of the room are either by digging a hole through the soil on the ground or by climbing to a window that you can break. Sadly, digging a hole in the ground would take too long and you would starve to death. On top of that, the window is far too high for you to reach by jumping. How will you escape?

2.   Hundreds of legs but can't walk. When it's dirty everything else is clean. What is it?

41

3. This is the time of day that is the same forwards or backwards. What is it?

4. No matter how careful you are, you will always look over this. What is it?

5. If thrown out the window, you get a sad wife. If it's in the middle of a door, you have a generous corpse. What is it?

6. What starts the month of December only and is not a holiday?

7. What has three eyes that tells people if they can go?

8.   What question can have so many answers no matter when you ask and all answers could be right?

9.   Which of a car's tires does not turn when the car turns?

10.   You give this to others but work hard to keep it. What is it?

11.   People always ask for this but will seldom take it when offered. What is it?

12.   While they are dark, they go quite often. Without the sun they die. What are they?

13.   Not one person wants this but they can't afford to lose it. What is it?

43

14.	This is made of wood but you can never saw it in half. What is it?

15.	This ends with IT and begins with S. When you're in the middle it looks good. What is it?

16.	What is almost never borrowed but is almost always returned?

17.	What is often running without any legs. It doesn't need you but you need it.

18.	When you lose it, you do not get rid of it. What is it?

19.	This is something you have but always leave behind. What is it?

20. Just before morning dawns, you hear someone knocking at your door while you sleep. It's your parents who are visiting because they need help with their cooking. They need to borrow some mustard, celery, mayonnaise and Worcestershire sauce. What is the first thing you will open for them?

21. The mother of a girl named Jodie has three daughters, namely, June, and July. What is the name of the third daughter?

22. You find a computer in a room with a bomb strapped to the top of it. Close to the bomb are some pencils, a glass of water, and a robot figurine. When the bomb goes off, what object will be the first to get destroyed?

23.   You have 15 different species of fish all swimming inside a regular-sized fish tank. One day, 7 of these fish died while fighting each other. 3 of them swam away from the fighting and 5 sank to the bottom. After the debacle, how many fish are left?

24.   There are two men who began playing chess. After a while, they finished playing five whole rounds of chess. Strangely, both of them have three wins each to their scores. How did that happen?

25.   In a certain household, there are five brothers. All five of them were busy with various activities. Kevin was reading a book. David was cooking a meal. Francis was playing chess, and Mark was busy with the laundry. What was the fifth boy doing at home?

26.   Imagine you're driving a bus. As you reach your first stop of the trip, 7 people board your bus. On the next stop, 6 people alight the vehicle. Upon reaching the third stop, an additional 8 people board. Finally, everyone gets off at the final stop of the route. What is the color of the driver's eyes?

27.   These things bake in the sun. On the other hand, they get broken when placed in the hands. Also, they are stepped on with the feet. Strangely, the are eaten with the mouth. What are they?

28.   When this thing turns, everything that is outside can no longer come in. When it turns once more, everything that is inside can no longer come out. What is it?

29.   There are three engineers that claimed that Nancy was their sister. However, Nancy swears that she doesn't have any brothers. Which of the two parties are lying?

30.   Upon entering a dark and scary room, you find a lamp, a stove and a candle. With only one match in your pocket, what's the first thing you're going to light?

31.   You see two people approaching each other at the airport. As they walk towards each other you notice that they are identical twins. They even have the same clothes. Which of the twins will be the first to greet the other as they approach?

Sunny Gecko

32. Imagine that you live in a one-story house. This house is made of special "redwood". With that being said, what color are the stairs?

33. What is the one thing that knows all the languages in the world perfectly?

34. In a race, your efforts allowed you to match the speed of the person in second place and pass them. In what place are you?

35. Mary was scolding her son for cheating on a test. She needed him to admit his mistake. She said if he is lies, he gets no supper. But if he tells the truth he will a spanking. What did her son say to escape punishment?

36.   On an island, you find 12 men. All these men weigh the same, except one. This odd one either weighs slightly more than the others and you have to find which of the 12 men weighs different. To make matters worse, there are no scales on the island; just one seesaw. Take note, though, that the seesaw will break after being used three times. How will you find the odd one from the group?

37.   See if you can name three consecutive days. You are not allowed to use Sunday, Saturday, Friday, Thursday, Wednesday, Tuesday, or even Monday.

38.   Ten people, including yourself, are playing the jackpot round of a gameshow. The host has offered your group a chance to win by proving your intelligence. You are all to be lined up according to height and asked to face forward. The tallest

person stands in the back. Once you're lined up, black and white hats will be placed on your heads in a random manner. Each only gets one hat and in no particular order. The number of black and white hats will also be random. Once the hats are placed on your heads, you will be asked to guess the color of your own hat. If nine of you guess right, all of you will be spared. Take note that you cannot look behind yourself and you can only say one of two words, black or white. You are, however, allowed to team up and devise a strategy to tackle this problem. How will you save yourselves?

39.   A wealthy businessman had three sons. He wanted to leave his estate and money to one of them but wanted to make sure that his riches would go to the wisest of the three. He called them and gave all three of them the same task. With a handful of bills, each was to buy something that could fill the room. The one that could fill the

room to a greater extent would have the inheritance. The first son tried to fill the room by buying some sticks, but that didn't fill it much. The second son tried to fill the room using sticks; which didn't do a lot either. But when the third son gave it a try, he filled the room only using two things. What did he buy?

40.   A captain and his crew were out at sea. He ordered two of his sailors to look out to the East and to the West and had them stand on opposite sides of the ship to see better. Although looking at opposite directions, the two sailors could still see each other. How did that happen?

41.   A rich man wanted to leave everything he owned to one of his children. He devised a test to see which one of them was the smartest. He told all three of them that his estate would go to whoever could sing him half as many songs as he

had days to live. The two older sons could not do anything, simply because they did not know how many days their father had left to live and thus, they gave up. The third one, however, was able to figure out the answer and got the inheritance. What did he do?

42.   At the harbor a ship was docked with a full crew and a captain. They were about to set sail. People were at the docks too to bid the crew farewell. All of a sudden, the ship began to sink. Yet instead of panicking, everyone cheered and the whole crew was calm. Nothing was wrong with the ship and the weather was nice. What happened to the ship?

43.   A bunch of mushrooms were growing on a tree. This special mushroom grows to twice its size every day. After 50 days, the mushrooms have managed to cover the whole tree. How long did it

take the mushrooms to cover only half of the tree?

44.   You find yourself in a room with only two exits, both of which are dangerous. One door would lead to a room made from glass that magnifies heat. The heat was enough to instantly burn everything that went into the room. The other room had a fire-breathing dragon. Which room do you choose to get out safely?

45.   You're stuck in a tower that spans a height of 50 meters. The only item you have to help you is a 25-meter rope. You may rappel down the tower using the rope but that will only get you halfway down the tower. How will you get down safely?

Chapter 3 Brutal Riddles

Get ready with your fanciest thinking caps because this is where the most difficult teasers of the batch come. The riddles in this section are longer because they depict situations and problems that you will have to analyze.

1. It is the first day after winter and you find a collapsed man on the porch. Along with the man is a carrot, two sticks and a puddle of water. What happened to the man?

2. A man who that resides in a hotel chose to live on the tenth floor of the establishment. Each day he goes to work, he takes the elevator from his floor down to the ground floor where he leaves the hotel. When he comes back, however, he only takes the elevator to the seventh floor and then takes the stairs. When it rains, he takes the

elevator all they back up to the tenth floor. He doesn't like to exercise. Why does he do that?

3.   A man and his wife are in a car. They are in a hurry to get someplace. The man stops the car in the middle of the roads and runs from the car. A few moments later he comes back to the car to find his wife was unconscious with a stranger in the car. What happened?

4.   When this is heard, people change mood. It can be hard or soft, weak or strong, mellow or harsh. What is it?

5.   Back and forth this only knows. Biting is its only chore. What is it?

6.   What is never thirsty but drowns on dry land?

7.   This is as bright as a diamond but as loud as a storm. What is it?

8.   You see this but can never touch it. The closer you move to it, the farther it steps away from you. What is it?

9.   These can be as big as mountains but they swim in an ocean without water. What are they?

10.   When you go to your right, this goes to its left. When you raise your right, it raises its left. What is it?

11.   It is blue during the day but is black during the night. It contains life but you cannot drink it. What is it?

12. What can be colorful or colorless, full or empty?

13. What is both a mother and a father but never gives birth?

14. This is shot at everyday but still lives. You lose if you scratch it. What is it?

15. What has no mouth but is loud? It's as deep as a well but as round as a button.

16. This is all around you. It is visible but not removable. It fixes itself. What is it?

17. What has ribs and a back and a belly but not feet?

18. It helps some see but blinds others. It's in castles and mountains. What is it?

19. This is sometimes called crazy, but is good when you spread it. It is also great alone. It also makes you fat. What is it?

20. There was a man who was found unconscious in front of a store at 3 in the morning. A brick was found next to the man who was bleeding profusely from his head. When police arrived on the scene, the man was arrested as he was taken away. Why was he arrested?

21. A boy was born in the year 2012 but became a father in 2019 at the age of 52. How is that possible?

22.   You are driving in car with your best friend to a wedding. Along the way, you meet the love of your life as well as your parents whose car broke down along the road. Your potential soul mate needs to get somewhere as well as your parents. How will you give everyone what they want including yourself?

23.   There is a basin in front of you that has about 30 liters of water. What can you add to the basin for it to have 20 liters of water?

24.   You see a taxi driver going against the flow of traffic. He doesn't slow down or change direction even if he sees police officers. The officers don't chase him either. Why is that?

25.   Imagine having ten horses. Each horse would need a stall in which to stay but you only have nine. What do you do?

26.   You have a rooster that sits on top of the roof of your house. It lays an egg one day and the egg rolls off the roof. Is the egg going to roll off the left side or right side of the house?

27.   A man strides into a bar that sells drinks but only asks for a single glass of water. The barkeep responds by suddenly shouting at the poor man. After being yelled at, the man smiles and says thanks to the barkeep and then leaves. What happened?

28.   A well-dressed barber left his home to work one day. As he was walking it started to rain. Since

he forgot his umbrella, he got wet all over except his hair. Not a single strand got wet. How did that happen?

29. A contestant in a game show was playing the final round wherein she could win a prize. The host asked her a million-dollar question. You have a kilogram of steel and a kilogram of paper. Which of the two is heavier?

30. An exotic pet dealer was travelling to see a client. He had a fox, a hen, and a bag of seeds with him. In order to reach his customer, he needs to cross a river. There is only one boat at the river which only has enough space for the dealer and one other thing. If dealer leaves the wolf alone with the hen, the wolf will eat the hen. The hen will also eat the seeds if left alone with them.

How will the dealer manage to get all of them across the river?

31.   A captain on a Japanese ship at sea decided to oil certain parts of the engine. Before doing so, he placed his wedding ring on his desk so that he wouldn't drop it into the engine while he was working. When the captain came back from his chore, his ring had been stolen. The captain had several suspects in mind. When he approached the cook, the cook said he was making the ship's next meal while the captain was away. When the captain asked the navigator, the navigator said he was out on deck, ensuring their bearings. Finally, when he asked his seaman, the seaman said he was busy on the mast because he noticed that the flag on the ship was installed upside down. After hearing all alibis, the captain knew who stole the ring. Who stole the ring?

32.   While walking along the road you come across a fork that splits into two. One path leads to safety while the other leads to a dangerous forest from which there is no escape. On the same fork you also find twin sisters that help travelers find their way. They know which is which among the two paths. The thing is, you can only ask one sister only one question. To make matters more interesting, one sister only tells the truth while the other sister would only tell lies. You don't know which sister is which either. What question do you ask and to whom do you ask it in order to choose the right path?

33.   You have a basket containing half a dozen eggs which you plan to distribute to six of your closest friends. After giving away one egg to one person, how is it so that there is still one more egg left inside the basket?

34.   In a hospital, an expectant mother gives birth to a healthy pair of boys. They were born within seconds of each other and had the same features, yet the babies are not called twins. How can that be?

35.   A certain Mr. Brown lost his gold watch inside the household on a Sunday afternoon. The police rounded up all the people inside the house for questioning. Mr. Brown's wife said she was in another room reading a book. Their butler indicated that he was washing the family car. The gardener claimed that he was tending to the weeds in the garden. The chef said he was preparing breakfast for the family. Who stole the ring?

36.   Two sons stand to inherit a fortune from their recently-deceased father. One thing holding back

the inheritance is the condition that the two brothers hold a race with their horses with the slower horse getting the inheritance. After several races wherein neither horse was moving out of fear of winning, the brothers decided to consult the family lawyer. After a few words, the brothers raced again; this time eagerly trying to beat each other. What did the lawyer say to make them act like that?

37.   You encounter a magician at the county fair. He challenges you, saying that if he can write your weight on a small sheet of paper, you would have to pay him 100$. If he could not write your weight on the paper, he would pay you the 100$. After checking to see if there are any scales, you take the challenge. You can always lie about your weight and claim the money. As soon as the magician hands you the paper, you concede defeat and pay. How did the magician win?

38. You and your friends are being chased by zombies that run at a set pace. There are four of you running away. The only way back to safety is cross a wooden bridge and to cut if off once all of you are safely across. Sadly, the bridge can only accommodate two people at a time. On top of that, it is dark and you only have one lamp to light the way. By your calculations, it will take the zombies 17 minutes to catch up to you. That means you have 17 minutes to make sure everyone gets across. You can cross the bridge in 1 minute. Sarah can cross the bridge in 2 minutes. Gary can cross the bridge in 8 minutes while Edward needs 10 minutes to cross. While you can only walk two people across the bridge, the lamp can only be used in one-way trips, meaning it has to come back to the start to escort the next person crossing. How will you cross the bridge in time before the zombies reach you?

39.   A hard-working man travels to myriad countries even without a passport. Instead of being questioned, he is always greeted with a smile by the people he visits. How is that possible?

40.   Stuck on an island surrounded by mountains, Jack finds himself in the middle of a very dense forest. In fact, the whole island is covered in forest. Unfortunately, a strong wind comes from the western side of the island along with some lightning. The lightning hits one of the trees on the western end of the island and catches fire. With the wind howling eastward from the west, the fire will eventually burn the entire island. What can Jack do to survive the fire?

41.   At a bar, a rich businessman is enjoying his fill of alcohol while a poor man takes notice of him. The poor man approached the rich man and asks

about his money. The rich man obliges and explains his job. After that the poor man brags. "I know every song in the world. I bet you all the money in your wallet right now that I can sing a song with any person's name in it.". The rich man laughs and humors the poor man. "Sing a song with my daughter's full name in it. Her name is Nicolette Alexandra Rodriguez-Rogers.". The poor man laughed and started to sing. After singing, the rich man paid the poor man all his money. What did the poor man sing?

42.　You're in the jackpot round of a gameshow you joined. You stand to win a free car or a goat. The game show host presents you three doors. The prized car is behind one of them while a goat was in each of the other two doors. The host explains you have to choose the door with the car behind it to win the car; choosing any other door would leave you with a goat. After making your initial choice, the host tempts you by opening one of the doors, naturally having a goat behind it. He then asks you if you still want to stick to the original door you chose or switch to the other door. Should you switch or not?

43.   Late one night, a man sleeping in a motel with his wife suddenly leaves the room to get to his car as he needed something. After he gets to his car, he sounds his horn very loudly and then goes back to his room. Why did he do that?

44.   An old but wise customer entered a diner and seats himself next to the window. The waitress approaches him ask what he wanted, to which the customer said "Just a cup of coffee.". The waitress went into the back and in a few moments produced a cup of coffee for the customer. A few moments later, the customer called the waitress and complained about finding a fly in his beverage. The waitress examined the cup and indeed found a

fly. The customer asked to have his drink replaced with another, to which the waitress agreed. She went into the back again and emerged with another cup. The customer took one sip from the cup and immediately knew that the waitress did not make a new cup but instead just removed the fly. How did the customer know?

45.   A jeweler reported a break-in at his store. He said almost all of his items had gone with the thief. When the police checked his house, there was a broken window. Inside the house was a big mess. There was shattered glass from the window outside and foot prints on the carpet inside the house. After investigating, the police arrested the owner for attempted fraud. How did that happen?

46.   Your friends have made you a nice birthday cake to celebrate the occasion. Thrilled by the cake, you decided to cut it and share it amongst

your 8 friends. One friend, however proposed a challenge: If you can cut the cake into 8 equal pieces using only 3 slices of the knife, he will make you another cake. How will you cut the cake?

47.   You were challenged by friend to pick a stone among two inside a small box. Both stones were of the same size and shape, but one was white and the other was black. If you were to pick the white stone, your friend would pay for your lunch today, while you would have to pay for lunch if you drew the black one. After agreeing, you noticed that your friend had placed two dark stones in the box. He approaches you and asks you to pick one. What do you do to ensure that you win?

48.   A tired lady is having some trouble sleeping in her hotel room. After switching positions and turning over, she decides to call the front desk and then asks to be connected to the telephone in

the room next to hers. The front desk agrees and connects her call. As soon as the tenant of the other room answers, the tired lady remains silent before dropping the call. After that, she returns to bed and falls asleep. What happened?

49.   During a party, your friend issues you a challenge to prove to everyone how smart you are. He hands you a pencil along with some instructions. You were to place the pencil on the floor in such a manner that not any one person will be able to jump over it. You have only the pencil to complete the task. How will you solve this puzzle?

Chapter 4 Difficult Answers

Welcome to the answers portion! The easiest ones of the batch are found here, unless you're so sure of your answers after seeing the questions earlier. As you can see, there's nothing too complicated here. See if you got any mistakes!

Difficult Answers

1.   An egg.

2.   A candle

3.   A sponge

4.   Are you asleep yet?

5.   The future

6.   A promise

7.   Your age

8.   A barber

9.   A bank

10.   Darkness

11. Your breath.

12. In the dictionary

13. A flight of stairs

14. A bed

15. A cold

16. A zipper

17. A coin

18. A deck of cards

19. A paint coat

20. A garbage truck

21. Silence

22. Light

23. Night

24. Day

25. A map

26. Your name

27. A towel

28. The letter "m"

29. Your reflection

30. Footsteps

31. Fire

32. A cloud

33. A post stamp

34. Nothing

35. A teapot

36. A wave

37. Time

38. A window

39. A doorbell

40. A piano

41. A library

42. A pillow

43. A temper

44. Your right elbow

45. A blackboard

46. A hole

47. Smoke

48. Fingers

49. A bottle

50. The word "wrong"

51.   Seven

52.   Halfway into the woods. After the rabbit runs past half, it's now running outside of the woods

53.   Nine

54.   The word "short"

55.   Move to a different spot

56.   Cutlery

57.   The letter "r"

58.   The word "bookkeeper"

59.   Pencil lead

60.   A Fishhook

61.   It's still Mount Everest

62.   That would be true if today is his eleventh birthday.

63.   An echo

64.   Everyone on the boat is married

65.   A mailbox

66.   A mountain

67.   Fire

68. Add the letter "G" to the beginning of the word. It will now spell as "gone"

69. A birthday candle

70. Trouble

71. A bullet

72. A watermelon. You eat the red part but don't eat the green parts.

73. A bar of soap

74. Charcoal

75. A lobster

76. The word "ton"

77. Your voice

78. A pig. It smells good when is cooked as bacon.

79. Ice

80. A piece of paper

81. Your breath

82. Anteater

83. Home

84. A clock

85. An onion

86. Sing language

87. A mirror

88. A clock

89. A joke

90. A chick inside an egg

91. A glove

92. A porcupine

93. A fence

94. A kitten

95. The moon

96. The word "Dozens"

97. Yarn

98. A coconut

99. Tomorrow

100. A caterpillar

101. A riddle

102. A calendar

103. The letter "s"

104. The wind

105. The blink of an eye

106. Knowledge

107. A light swtich

108. The king of spades in a deck of cards

109. A stapler

110. Water

111. The past

112. A scarecrow

113. Loneliness

114. The word "eye"

115. An X-Ray

116. Live

117. The word "valley"

118. A piece of a puzzle

119. The ocean

120. Words

121. Fog

122. A flower

123. A teabag

124. The letter "a"

125. An iceberg

126. A Windmill

127. The color blue

128. A vacuum cleaner

129. Your skull

130. A balloon

131. A window

132. A microphone

133. Shoes

134. A railroad track

135. The letter "T"

136. A cherry

137. Water

138. A wheelbarrow

139. A key

140. A spider

141. A mirror

142. A boomerang

143. An envelop

144. An arrow

145. Fingernails

146. A pair of scissors

147. A tree

148. A book

149. The pupil in your eyes.

150. An hourglass

151. Soda Pop

152. Rope

153. A road

154. The letter "I"

155. Pea

156. Iron Ore

157. A cherry

158. Writing

159. Stove, Fire, and smoke

160. A desk

161. A snail

162. A piston

163. An apple

164. Wine

165. A full moon

166. Makeup

167. Screwdriver

168. Oil

169. An egg

170. A platypus

171. A Hearse

172. A frog

173. A shoe

174. A nose

175. Raindrops

176. Cheese

177. A Peanut

178. Sparsely

179. A minister

180. A tombstone

181. An eyeball

182. An excuse

183. A beat/beet

184. Coal

185. Leaves

186. The word "alphabet"

187. An automobile

188. The letter "r"

189. Grape

190. A beehive

191. Fake money

192. The letter "w"

193. Ice

194. Shoes

195. A donut

196. Europe

197. A cornfield

198. An alarm clock

199. Your word

200. A friend

201. Wholesome

202. A river

203. A cat

204. A dentist

205. A wedding ring

206. Dates

Chapter 5 Extremely Difficult Answers

Did you have fun struggling with the problems in this section? If you've jumped over to this section, that would mean you're either very sure of your answer and you want to check or you've given up and you want to see the answer that has eluded you from the start!

1. While digging a hole and jumping to the window are out of the question, you are still going to need the shovel. Instead of digging to create a hole, dig to create a pile of dirt. You can make this pile of dirt high enough and sturdy enough for you to reach the window and break it towards your freedom.

2. A broom

3. Noon

4. Your nose

5.   The letter "N"

6.   The letter "D"

7.   A traffic light

8.   What is the time?

9.   The spare tire

10.   A promise

11.   Advice

12.   Shadows

13.   A lawsuit

14.   Sawdust

15.   Suit

16.   Thanks

17.   Water

18.   Your temper

19.   Fingerprints

20.   The choices were meant to confuse you. Take note that the riddle said you were sleeping when they started knocking. That would mean the first thing you open are your eyes!

21.   The third daughter's name is Jodie. It was clearly stated at the beginning of the riddle that Jodie was one of the sisters in the riddle.

22.   None of the items near the computer will get destroyed earlier than the bomb itself; which becomes destroyed when it explodes.

23.   Despite the violence happening in the tank, you have to remember that all of the fish are still in there with nowhere to go. You're still left with 15 fish in the tank, although in different conditions.

24.   This is only possible if you say that each man played other people and not their partner.

25.   While the riddle only discussed the activities of four of the boys, Francis was doing something that required two people; playing chess. Therefore, the fifth brother was playing chess with Francis.

26.   The color of the driver's eyes are the color of your eyes. Take note that the beginning of the

riddle mentioned that you were the one driving the bus. Everything else mentioned is irrelevant.

27.   The answer is grapes. They become raisins in the sun. You squeeze out the seeds in your hand. You step on them with your feet to make wine and of course, they're eaten with the mouth.

28.   The answer is a key. When you turn a key on the door, it locks people out. Turning it again locks people inside the room.

29.   None of them are lying. Engineers aren't exactly male all the time. There are female engineers. Instead of having brothers, Nancy has sisters; which makes both statements true.

30.   While all the items need the match to get lit, the match would need lighting first.

31.   Naturally, the twin that is more polite will do the first greeting.

32. Remember that the house was a one-story house. There are no stairs.

33. An echo can reply fluently in any language.

34. While it's impressive you passed the person in second place, you still haven't won. You're just in second place.

35. Mary's son said "You will spank me.". If she spanked him, then that would mean he didn't cheat because he was telling the truth. If she didn't give him supper, that would contradict his statement.

36. First, you'll have to put all twelve men on the seesaw; six on each side. This will bring down your suspects to half. Divide that group into two groups once more and use the seesaw for a second time. That should further narrow down your choices and also leave you with only three people. Finally, have any two of the three remaining men ride the seesaw. If the two men you chose don't tip the seesaw, then the third man not on the seesaw

weighs different. If one of the men tipped the seesaw, then he's weighed differently.

37.   While you can't use any day of the week, you can say yesterday, today, and tomorrow.

38.   Because you can only say one word and cannot use other codes, your codes would have to be in the form of your individual guesses. Remember that the person in the back will have to guess first. That person will also be able to see the hats of everyone else in front of them. Have him use his guess to signal the rest of the team of their own hats. If he sees an odd number of black hats, have him say black. If he sees an even number of black hats, have him say white. That will ensure that everyone else's guess will be correct. When the next person (the second tallest) will take their guess, they will have to think about what the tallest one said and what they see. Then the rest of the people in line will do the same thing. Base

their answers on the initial answer of the tallest person and what the previous people behind them have said.

39. The third son bought a candle and a box of matches. After lighting the candle, the light from the candle naturally filled the whole room.

40. While each sailor was looking at opposite directions, they weren't standing on the right side of the ship. The one looking to the east was standing on the western side of the ship while the one looking to the west was standing on the eastern side of the ship.

41. Since it was impossible to know how many days his father had left to live, the third son sang to his father every second day. By doing so, no matter what day his father passed, he would have already been able to meet his conditions of singing half as many songs as he had left to live.

42.   The ship was a submarine. The crew had begun their voyage by have the submarine dive.

43.   The mushrooms would have needed 49 days to cover half the tree since everyday they doubled. They would have covered half the dree on day 49 and then cover the full tree on the 50th day.

44.   Simply wait for nightfall and exit the first room. You won't have to be scared of the magnifying glass if there is no sun to fry you.

45.   All you have to do is to cut your rope vertically in half. That will double the length of your rope allowing you to scale the full height of the tower.

Chapter 6 Brutal Riddle Answers

This section contains all the answers to the brutal riddles in the third chapter. If you clicked the answer link after one of the riddles there, this is where the link will take you.

While the answers to the problems should be simple, short examples to the answers will be included as well, just in case other people don't immediately "get" the answers.

1.   The collapsed man is a snowman. Since it's the first day after winter, snow structures begin to melt. This is evidenced by the puddle of water, a carrot and two sticks which usually find themselves on snowmen during winter.

2.   The man is a midget; someone who suffers from a condition that makes him much shorter than a regular person. When he takes the elevator

from the 10th floor, he can reach the ground floor button, allowing him to go all the way down. Unfortunately, when he comes back from work, he cannot reach the button of the tenth floor and only reach the button for the 7th floor. When it's raining, he has an umbrella with him that allows him to reach the button for the 10th floor.

3.   The couple in the car is a husband and wife pair. They were rushing to the hospital because the wife was about to give birth. The car stopped in the middle because the wife had entered into labor. Desperate to call for help, the man left the car in order to get a doctor from the hospital to the car. Sadly, when came back, his wife became unconscious in childbirth but was able to give birth to their newborn. Since the husband and his child have never met before, the baby is a stranger.

4.   Music

5.   A saw

6.   A fish

7.   A waterfall

8.   The horizon

9.   Asteroids/meteors

10.   A reflection in the mirror

11.   Seawater

12.   A glass

13.   A tree

14.   The cue ball

15.   A bell

16.   Skin

17.   A ship

18.   Sand

19.   A peanut

20.   The man was trying to rob the store, given the questionable hours in which he was found. The man was trying to break a bullet-proof window using a brick to gain entrance into the store. Fortunately, his plan backfired as he wasn't aware of how sturdy the glass was. The brick bounced off the

glass and hit the robber in the head, causing him to fall to the ground.

21.   While it is undeniable the boy was born in the year 2012, the riddle did not say that the boy became a father in the year 2019. It just said 2019. In truth, 2019 is a room in a hospital.

22.   In order to get your friend to the wedding, offer a ride to your parents and get to spend time with the love of your life, you're going to have to get out of the car. Leave your friend to drive your parents. That would leave you and your soulmate together, albeit without a car, but at least together.

23.   All you have to do is to add a hole to the basin so that it loses water.

24.   Although he was a taxi driver, the man wasn't driving. He was walking on the sidewalk against incoming traffic, which is not a violation.

25.   Don't think of the horses as actual horses. Each letter of the phrase "ten horses" can fit in one stall (or space). Therefore, you have t-e-n-h-o-r-s-e-s.

26.   This is a trick question. Roosters cannot lay eggs.

27.   The man who went to bar was suffering from a case of the hiccups and wanted water to get rid of them. Instead of getting him water, the barkeep startled the man by shouting at him, which is another way to cure hiccups.

28.   The barber was bald. He didn't have any hair that would get wet.

29.   Although one seems lighter than the other, remember that you have a ton of each. That means they both weigh the same.

30.   The dealer has to first cross with the hen, leaving the wolf and the seeds on one side. After crossing with the hen, the dealer goes back to

fetch the wolf. Once he makes it across with the wolf, he has to travel back to where the seeds are with the goose in the boat because the wolf might eat the hen. Now the dealer has the wolf on the other. Next, the dealer has to leave the goose alone at the starting point and carry the seeds with him across. When he makes it across, he can leave the seeds with the wolf again. This leaves him free to come back for the hen without losing anything

31.   While all three alibis of the crew sounded reasonable at the start, one had a glaring mistake. Take note that the riddle indicated that this was a Japanese ship. The seaman said that he was fixing the flag of the ship because it was installed upside-down. If you would take a look at the Japanese national flag, it would look the same whether it was upside down or not. Clearly the seaman was lying.

32.   While this may seem daunting at first, the solution is surprisingly simple. Ask any sister what their sister would say if you asked them which is the safe path. If you had asked the lying sister, she would have told you which path the honest sister would say; but because she always lies, she would tell the opposite. On the other hand, if you ask the sister that always tells the truth, she would say what her lying sister would say, without changing anything. That would cause them to give the same answer; the wrong path. All you have to do now is to go the path opposite of what either sister you ask.

33.   The last person to which you gave an egg took the basket as well, leaving the egg in the basket.

34.   The mother did not give birth to just two boys. She gave birth to three, making them triplets instead of twins.

35. The chef was the culprit. All of the other alibis made sense, except his. Take note that the crime happened in the afternoon, past lunch and past breakfast, yet the chef claimed he was making breakfast at that time.

36. The lawyer told the brothers to swap horses. Since the condition was the brother with the slower horse got the inheritance, each boy would try to win with their brother's horse in order for their own horse to be declared the slower one and win the inheritance. The condition didn't say anything about the boy riding the losing horse.

37. The magician didn't write a number on the paper. Instead he wrote the words "your exact weight" on the paper, fulfilling the conditions on which you both agreed.

38. The first pair to cross the bridge should be the fastest ones, you and Sarah. That trip would take two minutes because you have to hold the

lamp and slow down for her. Once you are across the bridge, you have to take the lamp back to the other two who are left behind. That puts you at three minutes. Give the lamp to Gary and have him escort Edward across the bridge. That trip will take a full ten minutes because Edward is slow and Gary needs to keep up with him because he has the lamp. That puts you at thirteen minutes when Edward crosses. Now you're the only one left on one side of the bridge and the lamp is on the other. Have Sarah come back for you. She will take two minutes to cross the bridge with the lamp. That puts you at 15 minutes. Take the last trip across the bridge with Sarah for another 2 minutes, exactly taking 17 minutes before the zombies reach you and your friends at the bridge.

39.   The hard-working man works for the postal service. He doesn't necessarily leave the country. He simply visits the embassies of various

countries and delivers mail to them. He doesn't need a passport for that.

40.　Since Jack cannot escape the island, he would have to create a safe space for him from the calamity. He can do that by starting his own fire on the eastern side of the forest. He can take a piece of wood and set it ablaze with the fire and take it to the other side of the island. Once that side starts to burn, two fires will now be approaching each other, meeting in the middle. Once the two fires meet, there will be nothing left to burn and fire will die out.

41.　While the brag was very arrogant, the poor man kept his word. He sang a song with the name of the girl in it. He sang the "Happy Birthday" song to the rich man with the name.

42.　As you might have guessed, you're going to have to use a little probability to answer the question. At the beginning of the jackpot round, your initial choice had a 1/3 chance to win the car, seeing as there are two other possibilities. Those two other doors represented 2/3 of the probability. That probability changed when the host revealed one of the doors. The remaining two doors that had 2/3 probability were now narrowed to one. That means the other door had the 2/3 probability compared to the original door you picked which only had 1/3. Your chances of winning the car are better if you switched doors.

43.   The poor man had forgotten the number to his own room. His wife was deaf as well so she wouldn't hear it even if he called her. Instead, he sounded his car horn so that everyone would wake up and turn on their lights. By doing so, all he had to do was to see which room did not have their lights on, leading him to his room with his deaf wife.

44.   Before the customer found the fly, he had already added sweeteners and creamer to the cup. When the waitress came back for the second time, the customer drank the coffee she brought and noticed that it was already sweet and creamy.

45.   The jeweler was lying. If his store was really broken into, then the glass shards of the window would have been found on the other side of window which is inside the house instead of outside. The glass shards inside the house meant that the glass was broken from inside the house and not outside.

46.   While you are only allowed to use the knife three times, you may rearrange the cake in any way to prepare for the slices. Start by cutting the cake in half as you usually would. The second slice will create four identical pieces. Before you make the third slice, though, rearrange your four identical cake slices on top of each other. This will create a stack of four slices. Once stacked, the

third knife cut through the middle of the stack will create the eight slices you need.

47. Instead of picking the stone yourself, return the challenge to your friend. Have them pick a stone with the notion that whatever color stone the friend chooses, it will be safe to assume that the remaining stone in the box will be of the opposite color. Whatever your friend does, they will always get the dark stone, meaning you will always be left with the white one.

48. The poor lady couldn't sleep because her neighbor had quite the severe case of loud snoring. She asked to be connected to the room so that the phone call would wake this loud neighbor. After the neighbor answered the call and proved he was, in fact, awake, she was confident she could go back to bed to fall asleep before her neighbor went back to bed.

49.   Because you cannot use anything else except the pencil, you don't necessarily have to make the pencil tall enough so that no one can hop over it. Simply place the pencil flat in the room's corner section, right where two walls meet. In that place, no one would be able to jump over it.

Conclusion

Feel smarter yet? If you're at this point of the book already, you're probably seeing if this conclusion has any more hidden riddles for you to solve with your friends and family. Sadly, there aren't any more.

Now you see the value of riddles and brain teasers. They don't just keep you entertained for free for a few minutes. They also keep your mind sharp and on your toes. They also exercise your creativity and improve your reasoning. They also help develop confidence by allowing you to take the lead in solving something most people cannot do easily.

While they are mainly used as an activity, they most certainly go well with almost any social gathering; parties, dinners, gatherings, and even romantic dates. They are great ice breakers to set the mood!

While this book is no short list of brain challenges, there is still a vast ocean of riddles and problems for you to solve if you've really taken a liking to them. More often than not, people who have come to enjoy answering riddles so much begin making their own to see how they would fare if they became riddlers themselves!

Thank you

Before you go, I just wanted to say thank you for purchasing my book.

You could have picked from dozens of other books on the same topic but you took a chance and chose this one.

So, a HUGE thanks to you for getting this book and for reading all the way to the end.

Now I wanted to ask you for a small favor. **Could you please consider posting a review on the platform? Reviews are one of the easiest ways to support the work of authors.**

This feedback will help me continue to write the type of books that will enjoy reading.. So if you enjoyed it, please let me know! (-: